This book belongs to:

. . . .

For Jake – best friend, best dog. A.S.

For Tegan, who really can. L.M.

OXFORD
UNIVERSITY PRESS

Great Clarendon Street, Oxford OX2 6DP
Oxford University Press is a department of the University of Oxford.
It furthers the University's objective of excellence in research, scholarship,
and education by publishing worldwide. Oxford is a registered trade mark of
Oxford University Press in the UK and in certain other countries

First published as *Little By Little* in 2008
This edition first published in 2018

British Library Cataloguing in Publication Data
Data available

ISBN: 978-0-19-276853-7

10 9 8 7 6 5 4 3 2 1

Printed in China

Paper used in the production of this book is a natural,
recyclable product made from wood grown in sustainable forests.
The manufacturing process conforms to the environmental
regulations of the country of origin.

My First Milestones

I Can Swim

Amber Stewart • Layn Marlow

OXFORD

UNIVERSITY PRESS

Scramble was making a list.
A Can-do and a Can't-do list.

The Can-do side was much longer than the Can't-do side. On it was:

forward roly-poly

backward roly-poly

being kind to frogs

mud sliding

making very
good sandcastles

slippery-rock
hopping.

The Can't-do side was
much shorter. It just said . . .

swimming.

'Whoever heard of an
otter who can't swim?'
asked beaver.

'What? Not at all?' said bear.
'Not even a little? At your age?
All your friends can swim.
Whatever next?'

'Obviously being kind to otters is not
on bear and beaver's Can-do list,'
Mummy said crossly, when Scramble told her.
'And I bet their sandcastles are rubbish,'
muttered Scramble's sister.

Sometimes, Scramble would pretend he could swim, but really he was hopping — very, very quickly — along the river bed.

Other times, he would run along the river bank, trying not to be left behind by his friends as they spun and tumbled through the water.

But most days, Scramble would simply sit on
his favourite slippery rock, wishing and wishing
— from his whiskers all the way down to his toes —
that he could swim.

Every day, his mummy
would say, 'Today's the day
you're going to crack it.'

And every day — it wasn't.

Then, one sunny Monday, Scramble and his sister were
watching their friends jumping off the Highest-Ever Rock
into the Deepest-Ever Pool below.
'You have got to start small,' his sister said.
'Small?' said Scramble.

'Yes, small,' she said. 'Come on, today really is the day to start small. Believe it, little brother, starting small turns can't-do into can-do.'

So, on that Monday, Scramble started small.
He hopped along the river bed, keeping his toes
off the bottom just that bit longer every time.

On Tuesday, he did higher hops
and floating (with holding on) in between.

On Wednesday, Scramble did floating with no holding on.

And, on Thursday, he did a little kicking
and then a lot of kicking to the Halfway Stone.

On Friday, Scramble splashed and
kicked and swam the whole width
of the river — from one bank to
the other — all by himself.

And very soon (over Saturday and Sunday really),
that width became the length of the river from
Scramble's rock to the Deepest-Ever Pool.

Then the splashing and kicking turned
into gliding, and the roly-polies on the
river bank became underwater tumbling.

And, on Sunday evening,
as all his friends and family
gathered along the river bank
to cheer him on . . .

Scramble jumped off the
Highest-Ever Rock into
the Deepest-Ever Pool.

'I did it,' said Scramble to his sister.
'I can *really* swim!'

'You really can,' laughed his sister,
hugging her very wet little brother.

'You see. You started small . . .
and finished big!'

My First Milestones
Ten Top Tips

If your toddler is starting to swim, just like
Scramble in this story, here are some hints and tips.

1 Remember that bath time can be a great way to help your child feel confident and happy in the water before taking them to a swimming pool for the first time.

2 Involve your toddler in choosing their first swimming costume.

3 Try the costume out in the bath first (with a swim nappy, if needed). This will help your toddler get used to the feeling of the costume when it is wet.

4 Choose a swimming pool that has good facilities for toddlers, such as a shallow baby pool, dedicated parent and toddler sessions, and appropriate flotation aids.

5 Think about enrolling your toddler for structured swimming classes.

6 Always allow plenty of time to arrive and get changed before going swimming so that your toddler feels relaxed and ready.

7 Remember to share a small, light snack before swimming so that your toddler's energy levels don't dip.

8 Enjoy the one-to-one time with your toddler in the water.

9 Be encouraging and supportive as your toddler's water confidence improves.

10 Always allow your toddler to rest after a visit to the pool!